C2
THINK-A-GRAMS

EVELYNE M. GRAHAM

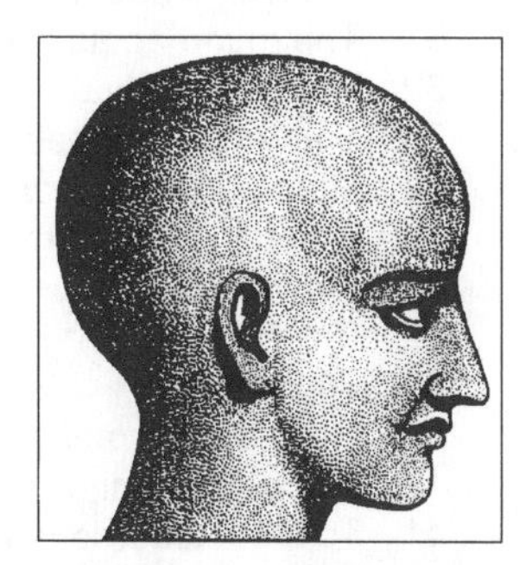

CRITICAL THINKING BOOKS & SOFTWARE
(formerly Midwest Publications)
P.O. Box 448 • Pacific Grove • CA 93950-0448
Phone 800-458-4849 • FAX 408-393-3277
ISBN 0-89455-432-8
Printed in the United States of America

TEACHER SUGGESTIONS AND ANSWERS

SUGGESTIONS

THINK-A-GRAMS are verbal picture puzzles. They can be posted individually, either daily or weekly, on a bulletin board to sharpen students' thinking.

In terms of difficulty, the A level is easiest, B more difficult, and the C level is hardest. Within levels, books 1 and 2 are of similar difficulty.

Each of the books in this series contains an answer key and 100 page-size puzzles. The puzzles provide teachers with an entertaining and challenging tool for coordinating right-brain thinking with left-brain memory. To solve these puzzles, the right brain analyzes the puzzle's symbology and the left brain recalls the common term or phrase depicted.

Since schools devote so much curricula to such left-brain activities as memorization and regurgitation, exposure to more right-brain experiences, such as these THINK-A-GRAMS, helps students develop skills in spatial relations, creative thinking, and problem solving.

Keep in mind that there is frequently more than one answer to a given problem. Encourage students to invent their own THINK-A-GRAMS for your classroom!

ABOUT THE AUTHOR

EVELYNE GRAHAM has 34 years of teaching experience—including all 12 grades—with a major discipline in mathematics. She spent 20 years as Supervisor of Mathematics for Chesapeake Public School System (Virginia), 6 years as Assistant Principal of Instruction at Chesapeake Alternative School, and 10 years as an extension instructor in Mathematics for Elementary Teachers for the University of Virginia.

Mrs. Graham holds an undergraduate degree with triple majors in math, religious education, and music, a masters degree in Mathematics Education, and a Certificate of Advanced Study in School Administration.

Mrs. Graham is a frequent presenter at state and national conferences and the author of books and articles about mathematics education and activities.

ANSWERS C2

1. Gallup poll
2. Up in arms
3. Too little too late
4. Fretting about trivia
5. Aw dry up
6. Cable overseas
7. Key problem
8. Small intestine
9. Put up or shut up
10. Bituminous coal
11. Drum tattoo
12. To win hands down
13. Stand up and be counted
14. To get things in focus
15. Fall in with
16. KOed in the second round
17. Time lapsed between start and finish
18. Seeing somebody on the side
19. Hip bone connected to the thigh bone
20. To skirt the issue
21. Leave before it's too late
22. Coming up roses
23. Head 'em up and move 'em out
24. Darkest before the dawn
25. Send in the clowns
26. Styrofoam insulation
27. A friend in need is a friend indeed
28. Camera on a tripod
29. Who's who in America
30. Football on Sunday afternoon
31. The round-about way
32. Yellow forsythia
33. Sought-after speaker
34. Murder in the second degree
35. One thing too many
36. Living down under the sea
37. Crash diet
38. Triglyceride
39. Getting back on track
40. Piece of my mind
41. To be overburdened
42. Brass trivet
43. Forecast
44. To be overcome with grief
45. Three-part harmony
46. Speak on your behalf
47. Tear apart
48. We're out to win you over now
49. Reincarnation
50. Working behind the scenes
51. Ill at ease
52. Upward and onward
53. This on one hand and that on the other
54. To be in Carolina in the morning
55. Border patrol
56. Forewarned is forearmed
57. To split hairs
58. Semiannual
59. Weasel
60. The bottom of the well
61. Locality
62. Keeping an eye on the girls
63. Torn between two lovers
64. You ingrate
65. Paradox
66. Unintentional
67. A rose by any other name
68. Vanished in thin air
69. Change in strategy
70. Junk pile
71. 64 K
72. Act infantile
73. Mixed feelings
74. Thinking back in time
75. Nerve endings
76. Deepest sympathy
77. An in-coming flight
78. Breathless
79. Reducing agent
80. Weaving loom
81. To fall in battle
82. Headlines on the front page
83. Mid-life crisis
84. Building values
85. Reinforcement
86. Traveling south of the border
87. I insist
88. Intense pain
89. Seminary
90. Tornado
91. Sign of the times
92. Home grown
93. Spreading infection
94. You break it, you buy it
95. All's well that ends well
96. Complete idiot
97. Right on schedule
98. Partial plate
99. Tale of two cities (Norfolk and Suffolk)
100. 'Til the end of time

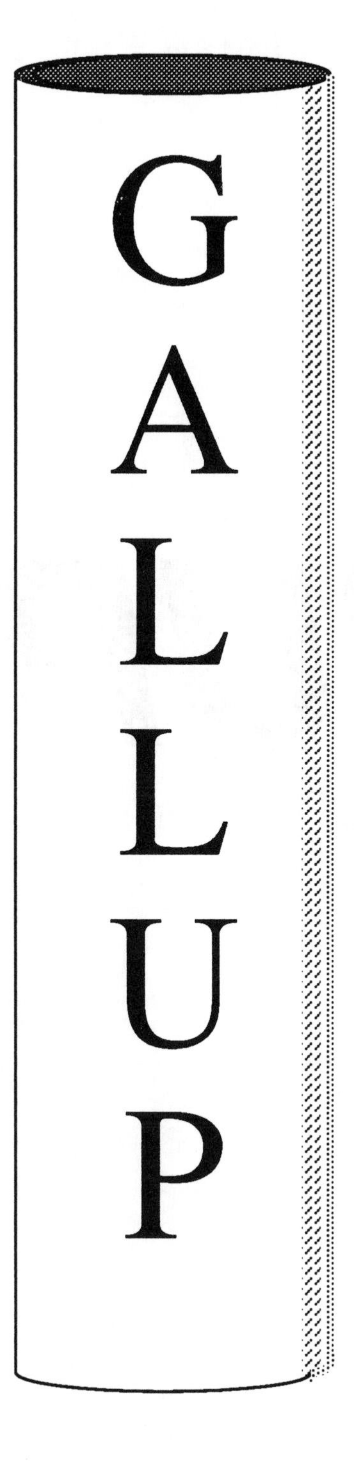
G
A
L
L
U
P

ARUPMS

LITTLE
LITTLE

LATE
LATE

TRIVIA
F-R-E-T-T-I-N-G-

Y
R
D
W
A

CABLE

C C C C C

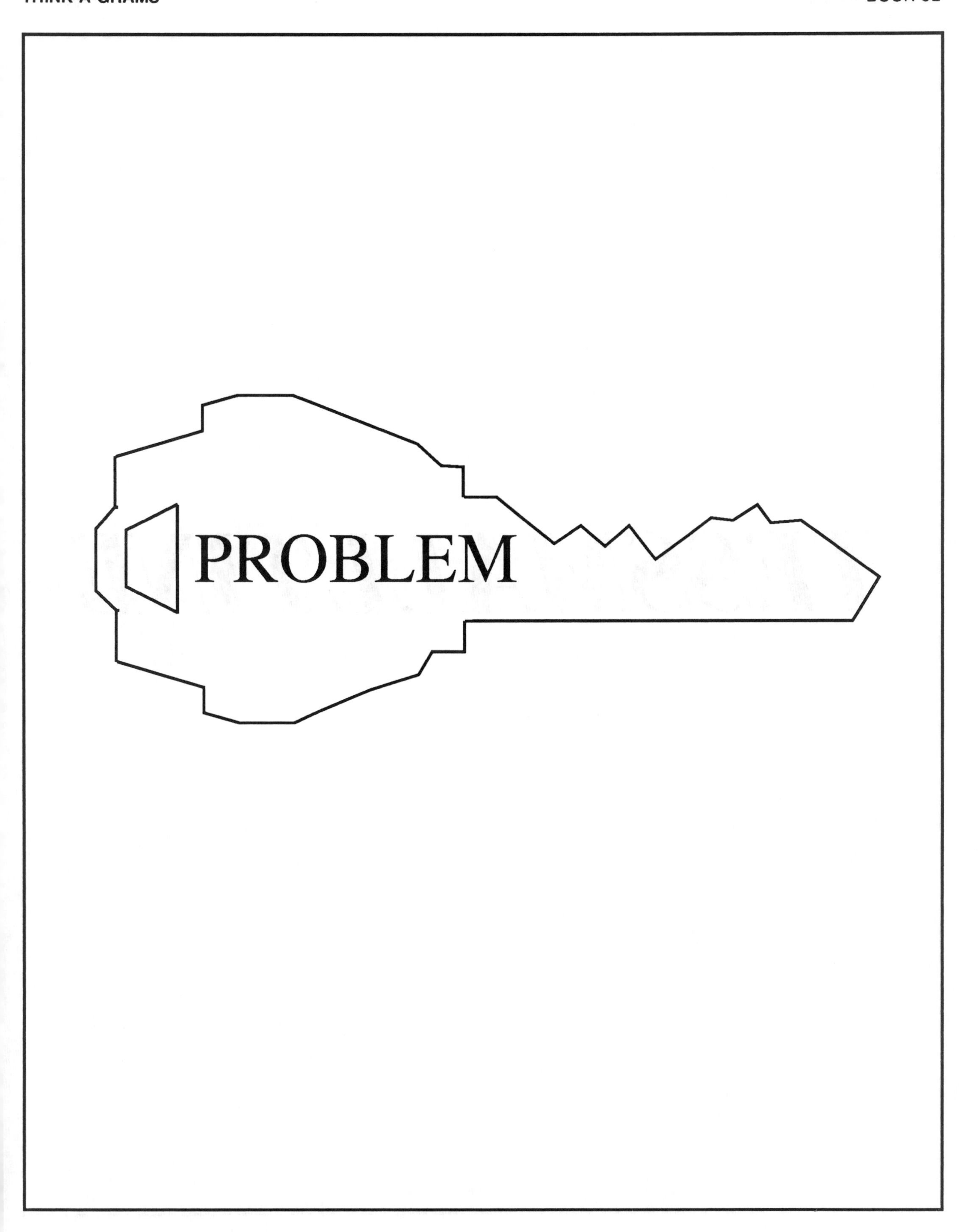
PROBLEM

TESSMALLTINE

T U P

R

T U H S

TUMINOUS
TUMINOUS

COAL

DRUM

TAT
TAT

WIN
WIN

H
A
N
D
S

D
N
A
T
S

B

COUNTED

GET
GET

FOTHINGSCUS

WIFALLTH

ROUND

ROKOEDUND

ROUND

START

TIME LAPSED

FINISH

C N SOMEBODY

HIP BONE

THIGH BONE

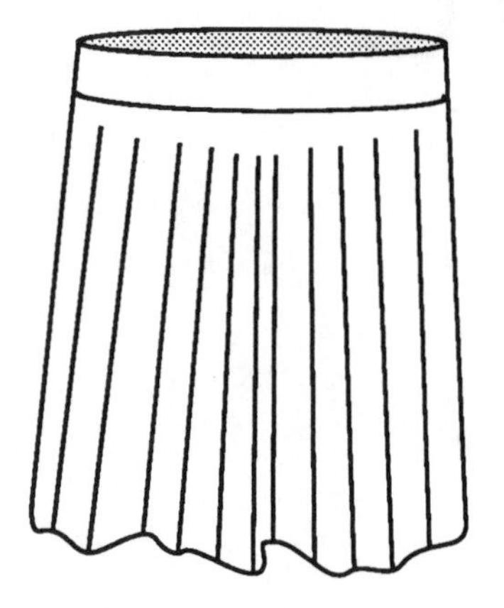

ISSUE

LEAVE IT'S LATE
LATE

G
N
I
M
O
C

ROSES

M E D A E H

MOVE EM

DARKEST *DAWN*

CLOSENDWNS

SULASTYROFOAMTION

NEFRIENDED

=

DEFRIENDED

CAMERA
POD POD POD

AMWHO'SERIWHOCA

FOOTBALL
NOON SUNDAY

O
U
N
D
R
WAY

YELLOW

SYTHIA
SYTHIA
SYTHIA
SYTHIA

SPEAKER SOUGHT

DEGREE

DEGMURDERREE

DEGREE

DEGREE

THING

MANY
MANY

SEA

L
I
V
I
N
G

D I E T

GLYCERIDE

GLYCERIDE

GLYCERIDE

GETTING
TRACK

MY

MIND

B B

BURDENED

BRASS

VET
VET
VET

1. ~~THROW~~
2. ~~TOSS~~
3. ~~SLING~~
4. CAST

B B

COME GRIEF

HAR

MO

NY

SPEAK
YOUR

B

—

2

TE AR

WE'RE

WIN WIN U

NOW

CREARNATION

WORKING THE SCENES

~~UNREST~~

~~TROUBLE~~

EASE ILL

~~COMFORT~~

D
R
A
W

THIS
ONE HAND

MORCAROBBLINANING

PATROL PATROL PATROL

PATROL PATROL PATROL

PATROL PATROL PATROL

PATROL PATROL PATROL

WARNED *ARMED*

WARNED *ARMED*

=

WARNED *ARMED*

WARNED *ARMED*

ANNUAL

SEL

THE WELL

CALITY

KEEPING I
GIRLS

ANTHONY

TORN

CLEOPATRA

GRATUE

DOX
DOX

TENTUNIONAL

ROSE

OTHER
NAME

ROSE

OTHER
NAME

ROSE

OTHER
NAME

A VANISHED IR

STR***ATEGY***

KKKKKKKK
KKKKKKKK
KKKKKKKK
KKKKKKKK
KKKKKKKK
KKKKKKKK
KKKKKKKK
KKKKKKKK

FANACTTILE

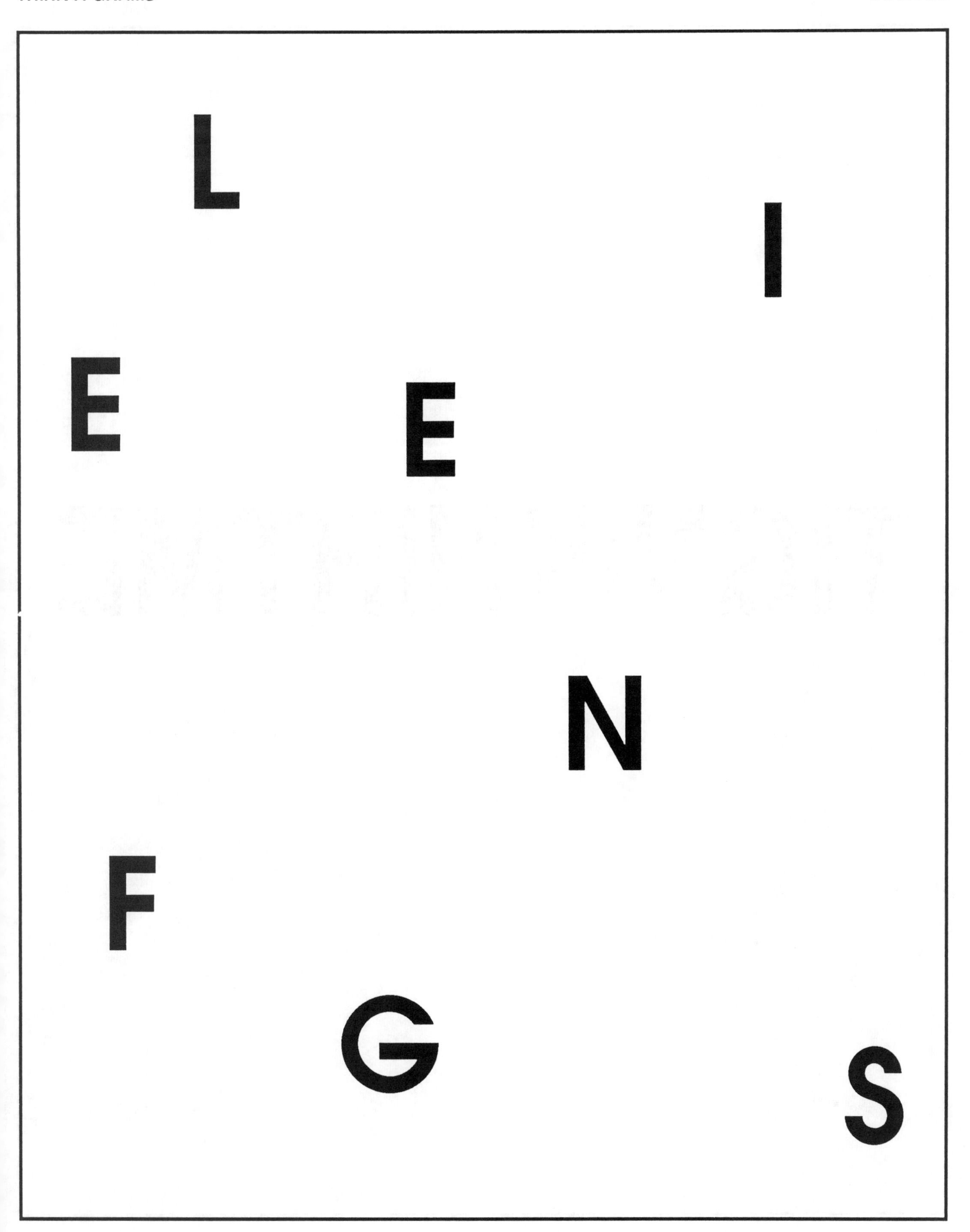
L
I
E
E
N
F
G
S

TIGNIKNIHTME

RVE *RVE*

RVE

RVE

RVE

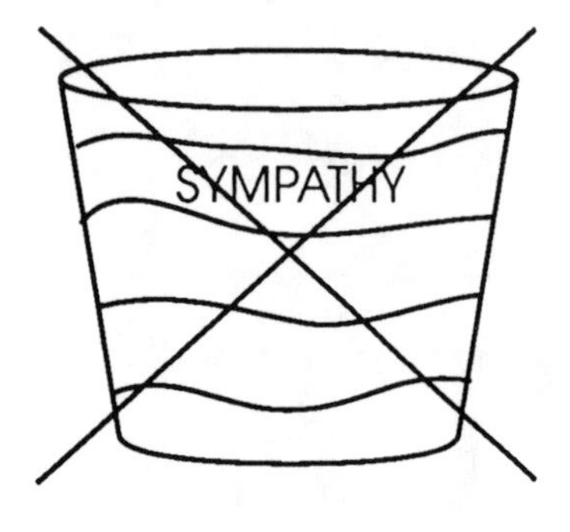
SYMPATHY

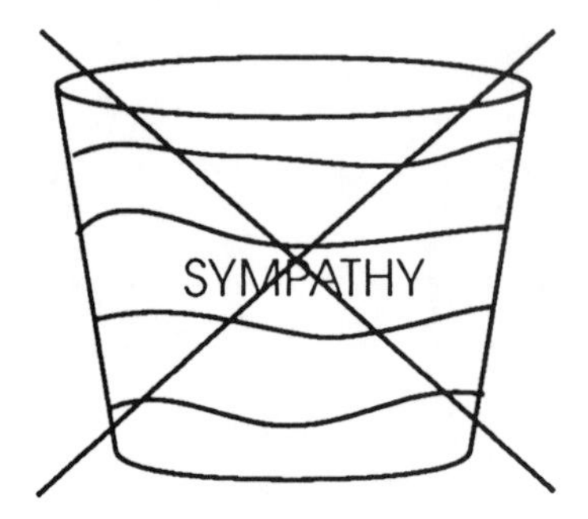
SYMPATHY

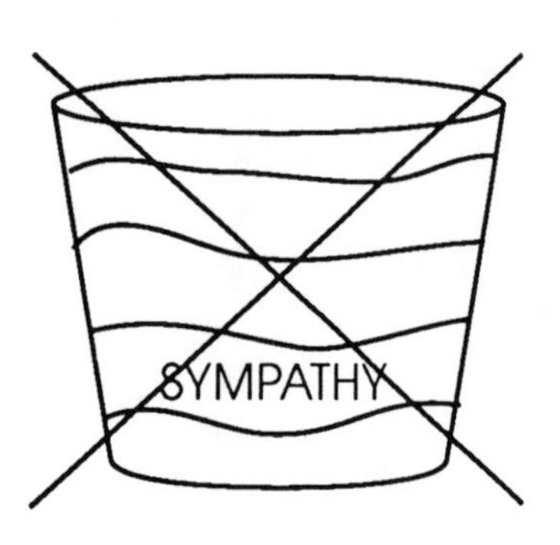
SYMPATHY

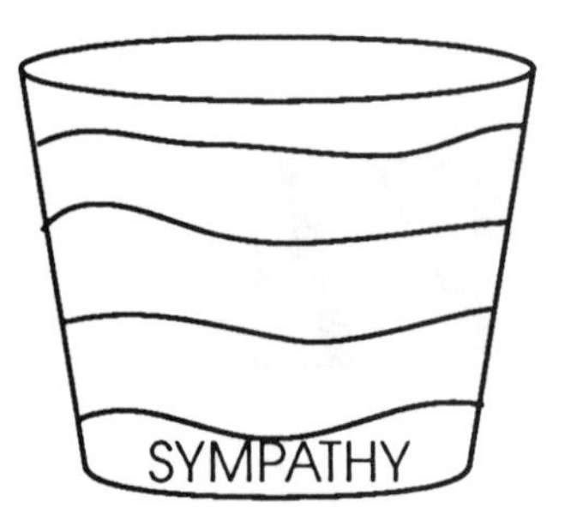
SYMPATHY

COMANING

FLIGHT

BREATH

-BREATH

AGENT

VING

LOOM

BFALLFALLATTLE

PAGE
PAGE
PAGE
HEADLINES
PAGE

LICRISISFE

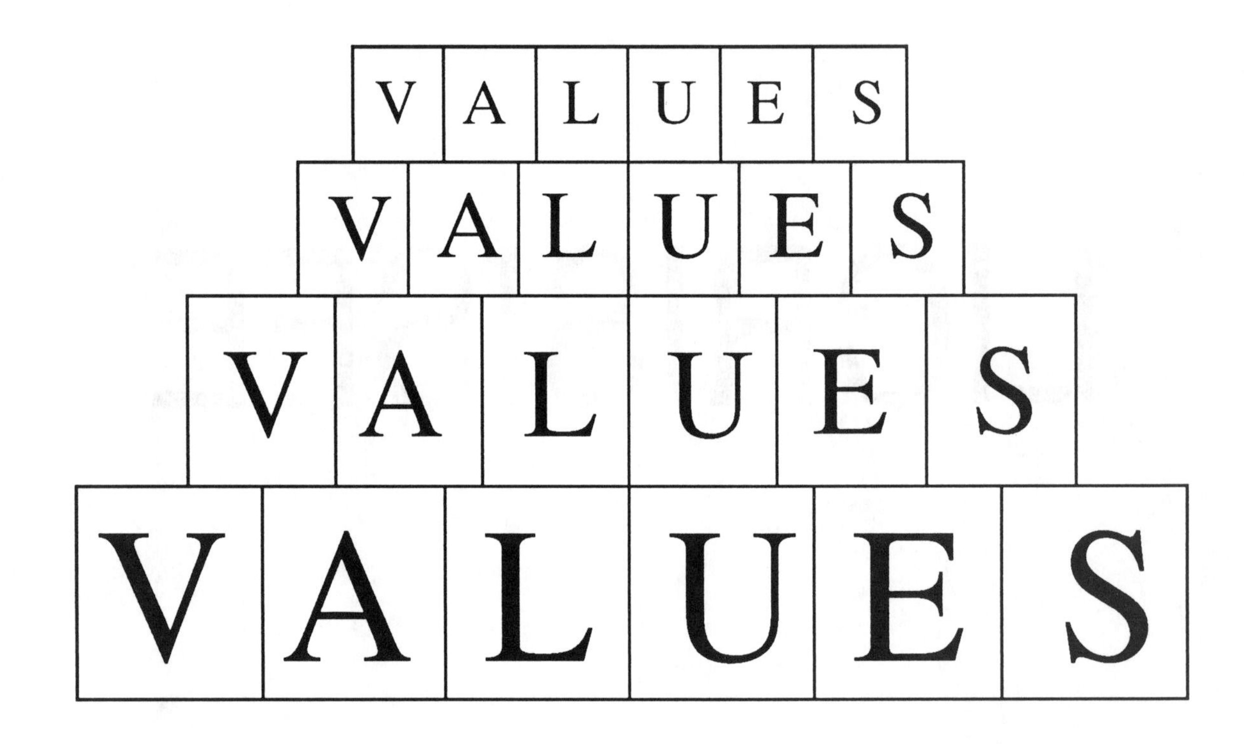
VALUES
VALUES
VALUES
VALUES

FORCEREMENT

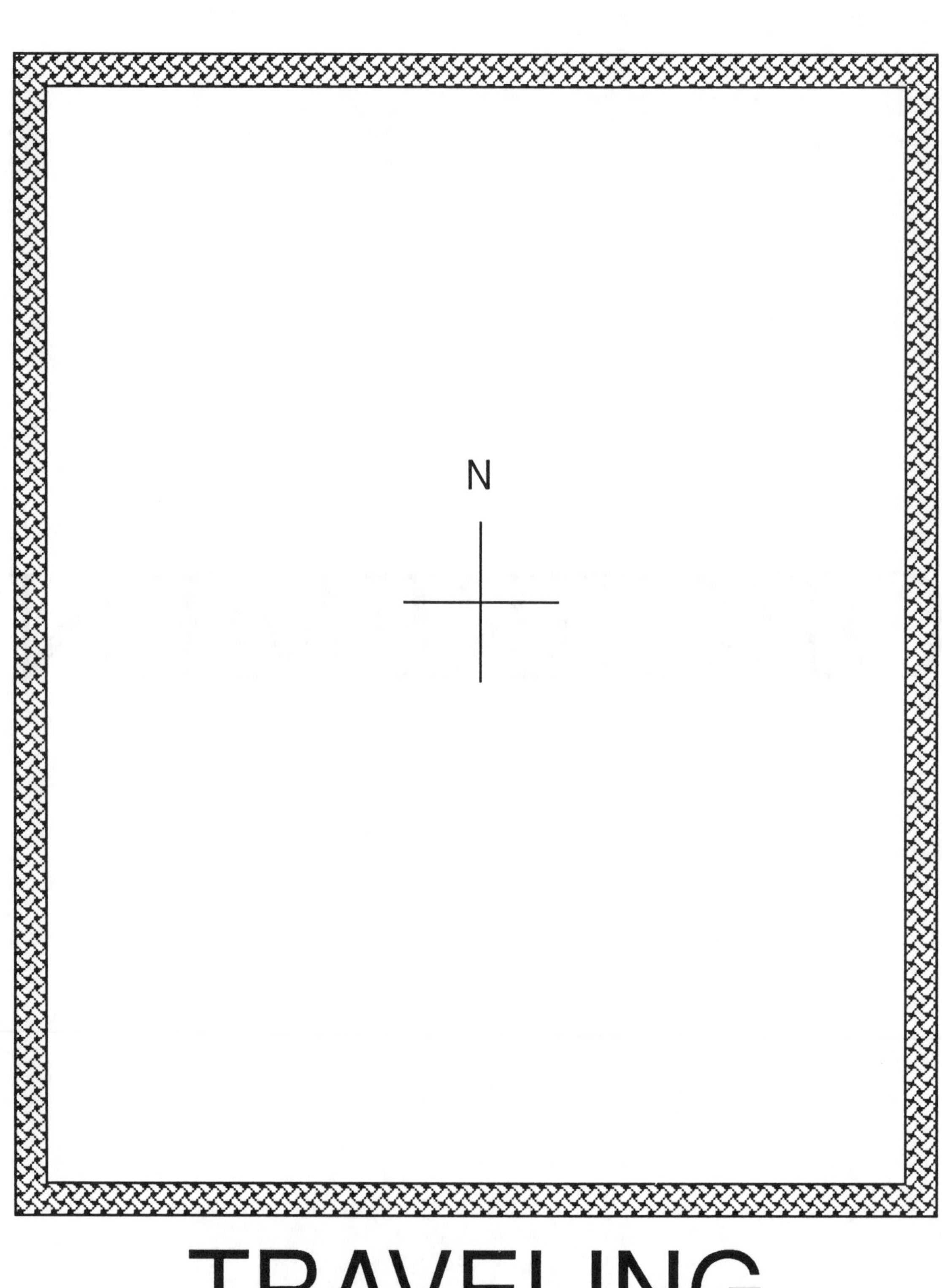

TRAVELING

SIIST

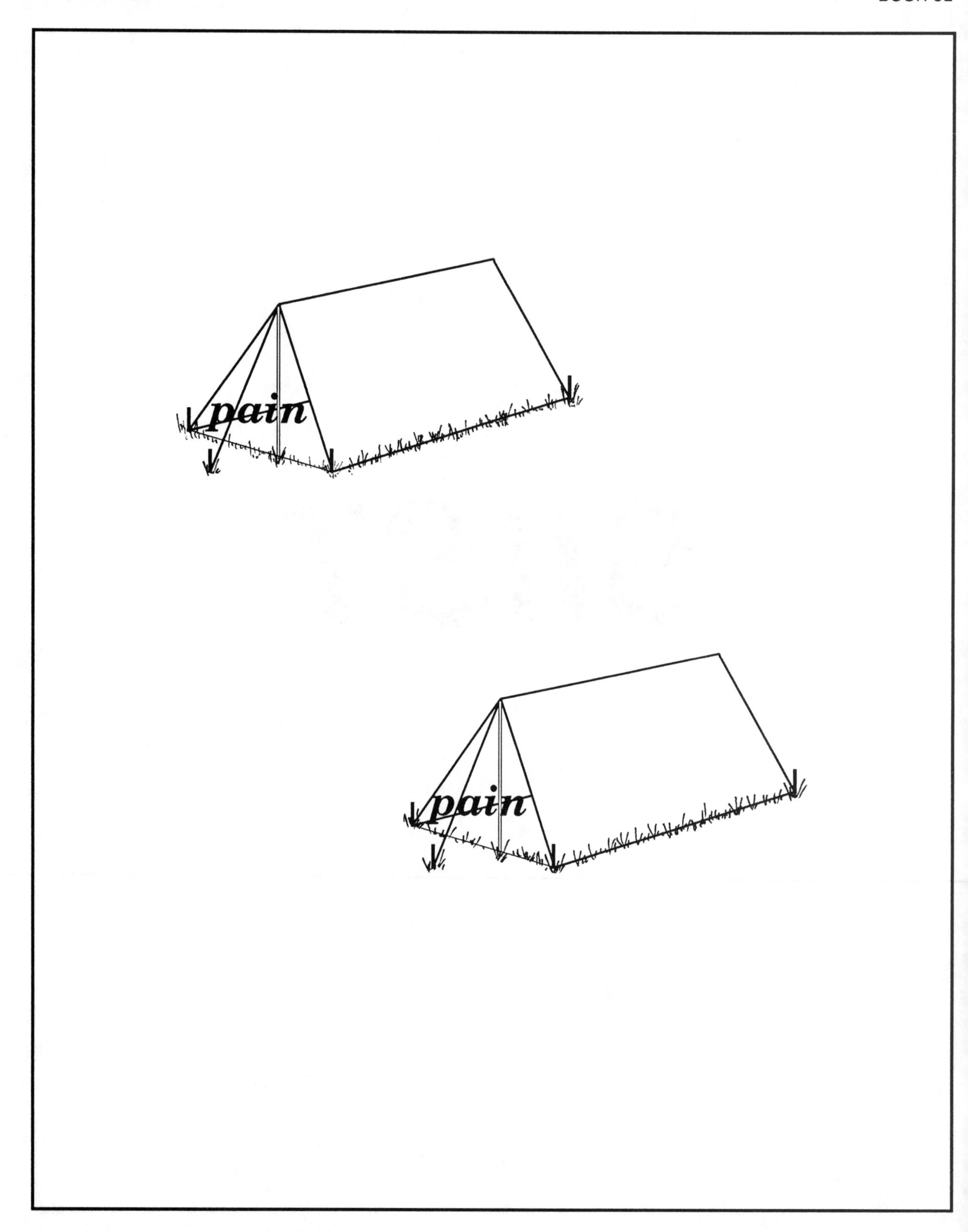
pain
pain

NARY

ADO

X X X X X
X X X X X
X X X X X

HOME

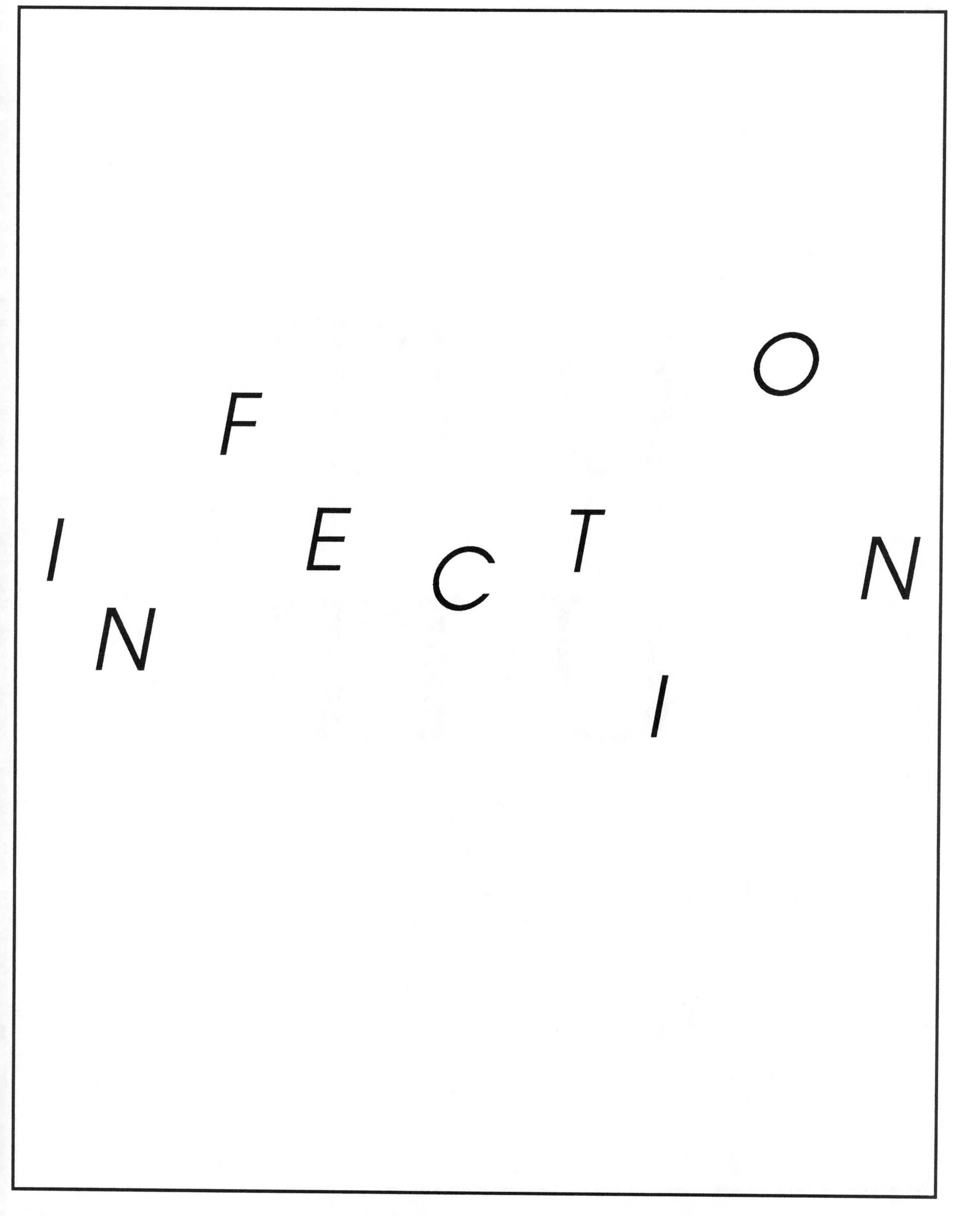
O
F
I E T N
C
N
I

U IT

U IT

WELLWELLWELLWELLWELLWELL
WELLWELLWELLWELLWELLWELL
WELLWELLWELLWELLWELLWELL
WELLWELLWELLWELLWELLWELL
WELLWELLWELLWELLWELLWELL
WELLWELLWELLWELLWELLWELL
WELLWELLWELLWELLWELLWELL
WELLWELLWELLWELLWELLWELL
WELLWELLWELLWELLWELLWELL
WELLWELLWELLWELLWELLWELL
WELLWELLWELLWELLWELLWELL
WELLWELLWELLWELLWELLTHAT

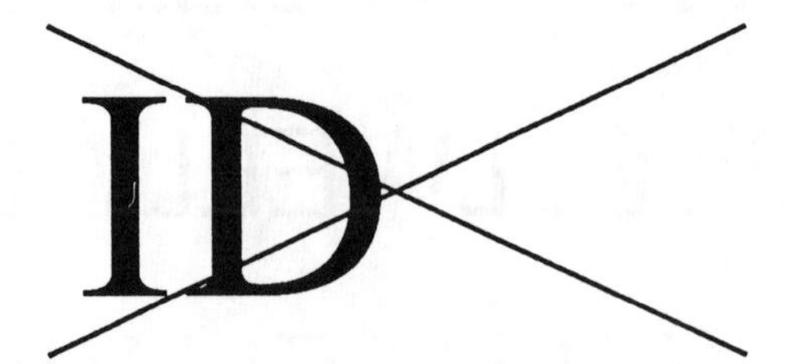

~~IDI~~

~~IDIO~~

IDIOT

Leaves
Arrives
1:00 P.M.
3:00 P.M.
2:00 P.M.
4:00 P.M.
3:00 P.M.
5:00 P.M.
4:00 P.M.
6:00 P.M.
RIGHT

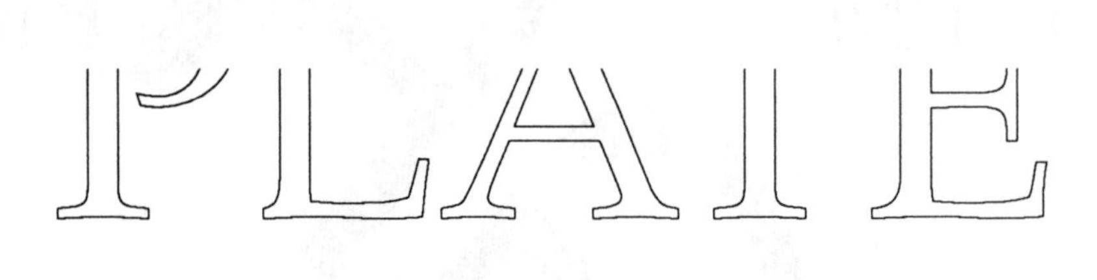
PLATE

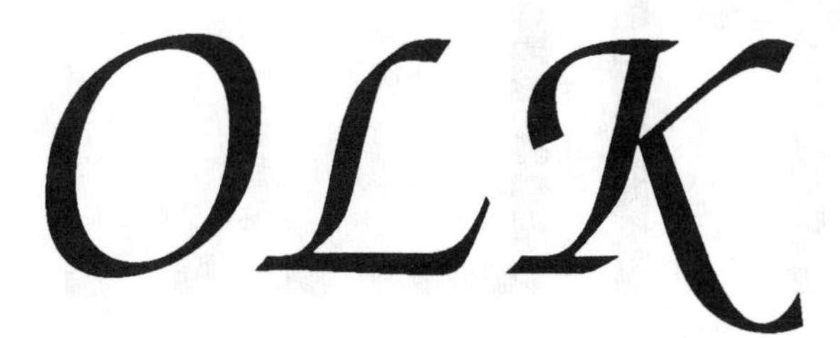
OLK

'TIL...E